How to Use the Viewer

light source   wheel   eyepiece

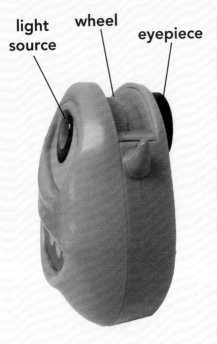

- When using the viewer, go to a brightly lit room or a window. Hold the viewer up to the light or window and look through the eyepiece to see the pictures. When using the viewer, do not look directly at the sun.

- Look through the eyepiece and turn the wheel until you find the picture labeled with a 1. Now you are ready to start reading Book One.

- The numbers next to the text in the book correspond with the numbers on the pictures in the viewer.

- Turn the wheel to the right as you read through the story to see the pictures in order.

- On some of the pages in the book, the images are in 3-D. When you see this icon **3-D** put on your 3-D glasses to see the pictures.

Disney · PIXAR

MONSTERS
UNIVERSITY

Book One:
Scare Students

adapted by Susan Amerikaner

illustrated by Disney Storybook Artists

3-D images by Pinsharp

Reader's
Digest
Children's Books®

New York, New York • Montréal, Québec • Bath, United Kingdom

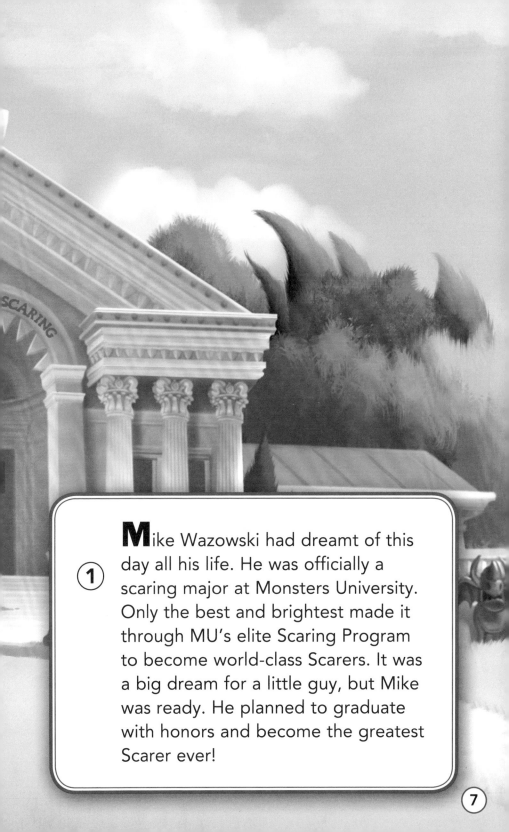

Mike Wazowski had dreamt of this day all his life. He was officially a scaring major at Monsters University. Only the best and brightest made it through MU's elite Scaring Program to become world-class Scarers. It was a big dream for a little guy, but Mike was ready. He planned to graduate with honors and become the greatest Scarer ever!

(1)

After he registered for classes, Mike checked out other fun activities and groups, including fraternities. He got a flyer about the Scare Games—the biggest event of the year. Sponsored by the Greek Council, this fierce competition proved which students were the best Scarers on campus.

On the first day of class, everyone was surprised when the head of the Scaring Program, Dean Hardscrabble, stopped by. She warned students that if they didn't pass the scare final at the end of the semester, they could not stay in the Scaring Program. The Dean flew off, leaving Professor Knight in charge.

James P. Sullivan, or Sulley for short, arrived late. Sulley's dad was a famous Scarer. The Professor expected great things from Sulley. He was big, scary-looking, and had an awesome roar. Sulley had natural talent. He didn't think monsters learned to scare; they just did it.

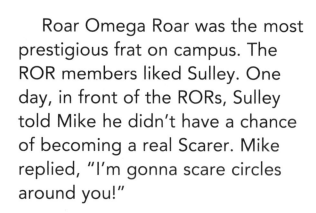

Roar Omega Roar was the most prestigious frat on campus. The ROR members liked Sulley. One day, in front of the RORs, Sulley told Mike he didn't have a chance of becoming a real Scarer. Mike replied, "I'm gonna scare circles around you!"

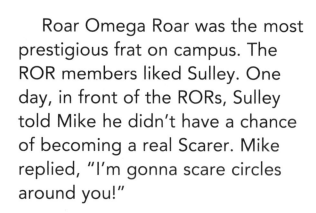

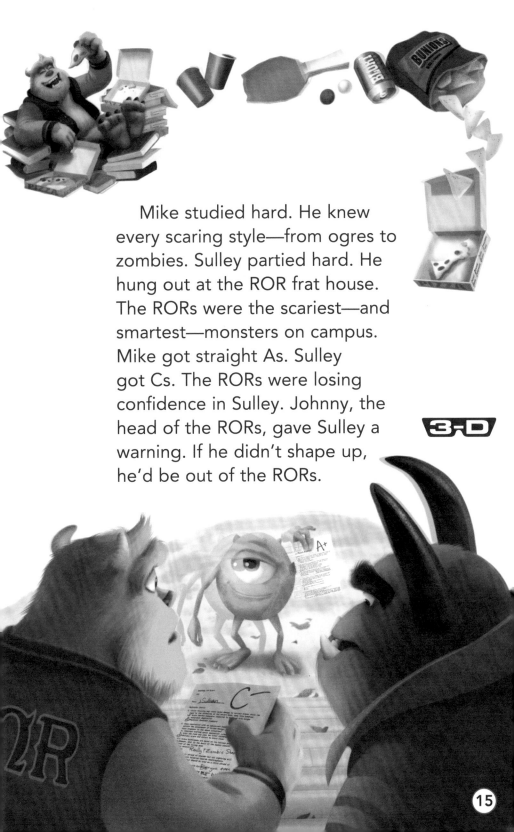

Mike studied hard. He knew every scaring style—from ogres to zombies. Sulley partied hard. He hung out at the ROR frat house. The RORs were the scariest—and smartest—monsters on campus. Mike got straight As. Sulley got Cs. The RORs were losing confidence in Sulley. Johnny, the head of the RORs, gave Sulley a warning. If he didn't shape up, he'd be out of the RORs.

It was the day of the scare final. Dean Hardscrabble watched. Sulley and Mike got into a roaring match and Sulley bumped into the Dean's prized scream can. It broke and released her famous record-breaking scream.

Hardscrabble gave Mike and Sulley their final scare challenges. She determined that neither Mike nor Sulley would continue in the Scaring Program.

The year went on. Mike and Sulley were forced to become Scream Can Design majors. Sulley blamed it all on Mike. He was furious. Mike was depressed and frustrated. One day, Mike threw a Scream Can Design textbook at his dorm wall. Suddenly, he saw the Scare Games flyer he had posted on his wall when he first arrived at MU. The sign-ups were taking place that day.

Mike rushed to Fraternity Row because competitors must be in a fraternity or sorority. Mike quickly joined Oozma Kappa. The OKs were the least scary monsters on campus!

Dean Hardscrabble agreed to a deal: if Mike won the games, his entire team would be allowed into the Scaring Program. If he lost, he would leave Monsters University.

The OKs needed one more player. Sulley joined the Oozma Kappas, too. Mike was not happy.

Continued in Book 2...